I DON'T LIKE

KAREN HAYLES

"I don't like fish."

"Hello, Whale. What do you eat?"
"Lots of fish," said Whale.

"Hello, Seal. What's your favourite food?"
"Fish of course," said Seal.

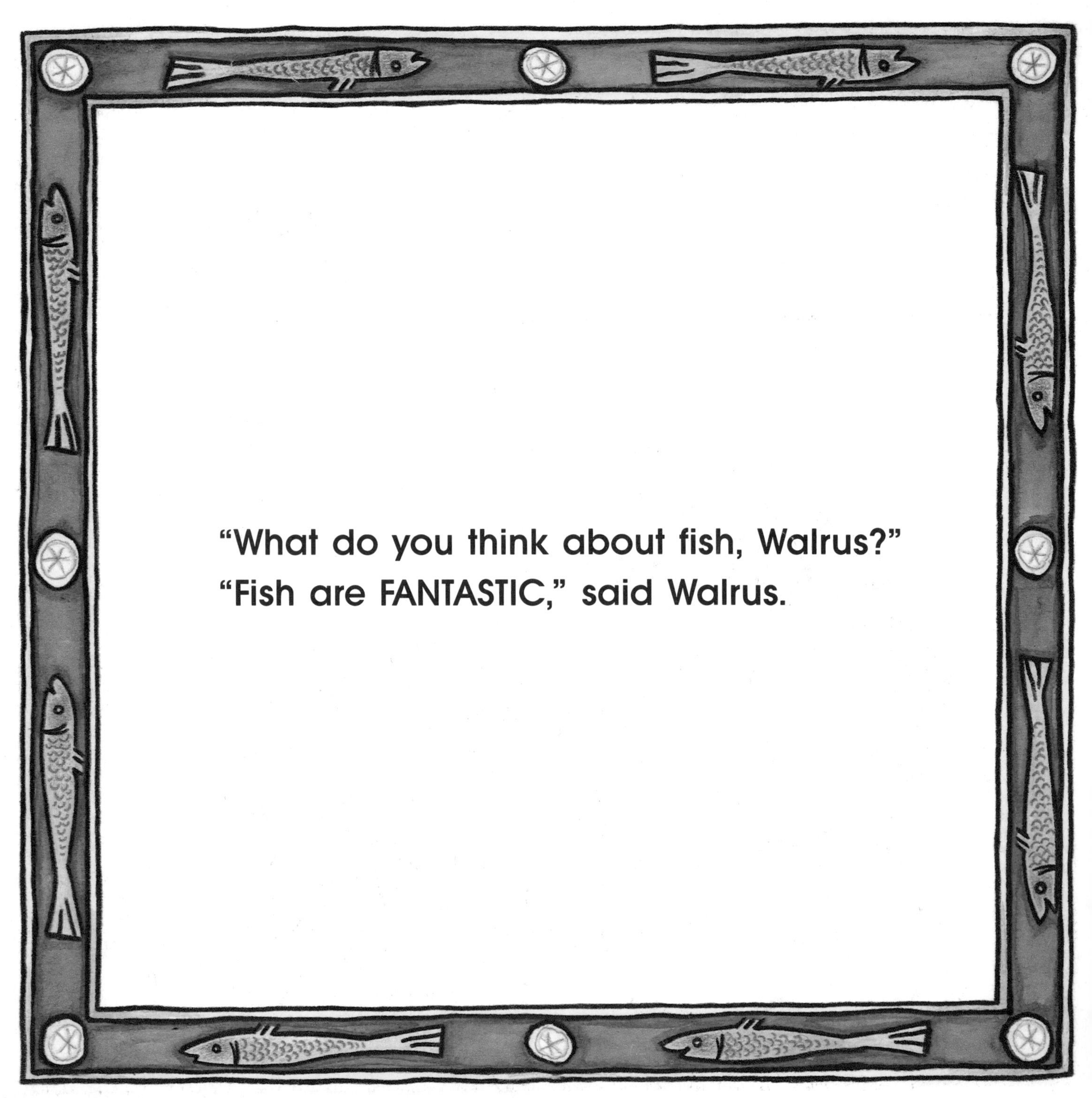

"What do you think about fish, Walrus?"
"Fish are FANTASTIC," said Walrus.

“Do you eat fish too?” said Polar Bear.

“Sometimes, but beans on toast is best!”

“I’ll tell my mum!” said Polar Bear.

"I know what we'll do," said Mum.
"Fish on beans on toast!"

"GREAT!" said Polar Bear.

BEANS
BEANS
BEANS
BEANS

BEANS